the music

glee

season two

4

volume

Published by
Wise Publications
14-15 Berners Street, London W1T 3LJ, UK.

Exclusive distributors:
Music Sales Limited
Distribution Centre,
Newmarket Road, Bury St Edmunds, Suffolk, IP33 3YB, UK.
Music Sales Pty Limited
20 Resolution Drive, Caringbah, NSW 2229, Australia.

Order No. AM1003233
ISBN 978-1-78038-037-7

Edited by Jenni Wheeler.

Printed in the EU.

www.musicsales.com

the music
glee
season two

4

volume

Wise Publications
part of The Music Sales Group
London / New York / Paris / Sydney / Copenhagen /
Berlin / Madrid / Hong Kong / Tokyo

Empire State Of Mind

Words & Music by Shawn Carter, Alexander Shuckburgh, Janet Sewell-Ulepic, Alicia Keys,
Angela Hunte, Sylvia Robinson & Bert Keyes

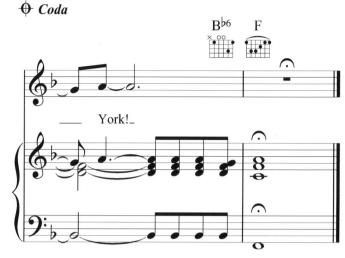

Verse 1:

Yeah, yeah, I'm up at Brooklyn, now I'm down in Tribeca
Right next to DeNiro; but I'll be hood forever.
I'm the new Sinatra
And since I made it here I can make it anywhere.
Yeah, they love me everywhere
I used to cop in Harlem
All of my Dominicanos right there up on Broadway.
Brought me back to that McDonalds
Took it to my stash spot, 560 State Street
Catch me in the kitchen like a Simmons whipping Pastry.
Cruising down 8th street, off-white Lexus
Driving so slow, but BK is from Texas.
Me, I'm up at Bed Stuy, home of that boy Biggie
Now I live on Billboard, and I brought my boys with me.
Say what up to Ty Ty, still sipping Mai-tai
Sitting courtside Knicks and Nets give me high fives.
Jigger, I be spiked out, I can trip a referee
Tell by my attitude that I most definitely from…

Verse 2:

Catch me at the X with OG at a Yankee game
Dude, I made the yankee hat more famous than a yankee can.
You should know I bleed blue, but I ain't a crip though
But I got a gang of brothers walking with my clique, though.
Welcome to the melting pot, corners where we selling rocks
Africa bambata, home of the hip hop.
Yellow cab, gypsy cab, dollar cab, holla back
For foreigners it ain't fitting, act like they forgot how to act.
Eight million stories out there and their naked city
It's a pity half of y'all won't make it.
Me, I gotta plug Special Ed I got it made
If Jeez is paying LeBron, I'm paying Dwayne Wade.
Thre-dice cee-lo, three-card Monte
Labor Day parade. Rest in peace Bob Marley.
Statue of Liberty, long live the World Trade
Long live the kingdom
I'm from the Empire State; that's…

Verse 3:

Lights is blinding; girls need blinders
So they can step out of bounds quick.
The side lines is blind with casualties
Who sipping life casually, then gradually become worse.
Don't bite the apple, Eve
Caught up in the in-crowd, now you're in style
And in the winter gets cold 'en vogue' with your skin out.
The city of sin is a pity on a whim
Good girls gone bad, the city's filled with them.
Mummy took a bus trip, and now she's got her bust out
Everybody ride her, just like a bus route.
Hail Mary to the city! You're a virgin
And Jesus can't save you. Life starts when the church ends.
Came here for school, graduated to the high life
Ball players, rap stars, addicted to the limelight.
MDMA got you feeling like a champion
The city never sleeps; better slip you an 'Ambien'!

Billionaire

Words & Music by Ari Levine, Khari Cain, Khalil Walton &
Phillip Lawrence

smil-ing next to Op-rah and the Queen. Oh,

ev-'ry time I close my eyes___ I

see my name in shin-ing lights.___ Yeah.___

A diff-'rent cit-y ev-'ry night.___ Oh,___

11

C#7

-er of   Forbes___ mag - a - zine,___

F#m   E   *D.S.S. al Coda II*

smil - ing   next to   Op - rah   and the   Queen.   Oh,

Drums

φ *Coda II*

Bm   A

I   wan - na be   a

C#7   **rit.**

bil - lion - aire___   so___   frick - ing   bad.___

17

Me Against The Music

Words & Music by Madonna, Britney Spears, Christopher Stewart, Penelope Magnet,
Terius Nash, Gary O'Bryan & Thabiso Nkhereanye

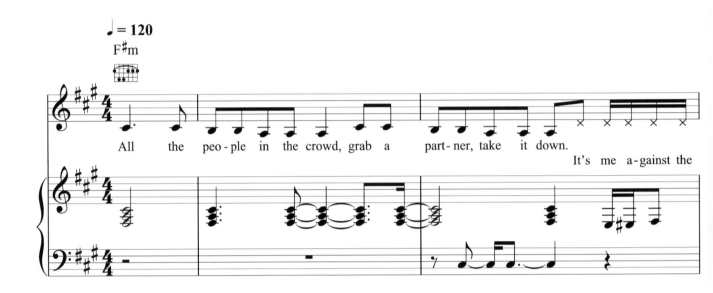

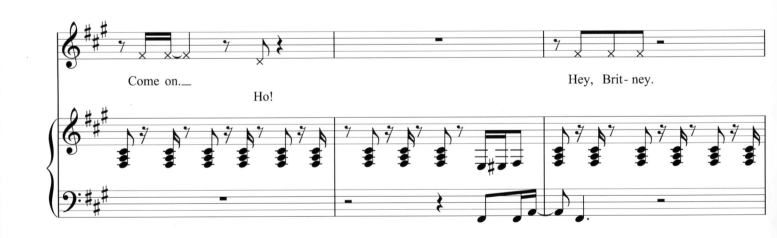

All my peo - ple in___ the crowd, let me see you dance.

(I wan - na see ya.)

1.

How would you like a friend - ly com - pe - ti - tion? Let's take___ on the song,___

let's take on the song.___ It's

you and me, ba - by, we're the mu - sic; time to par - ty all night long.___

All my peo - ple in the crowd. Let me see you dance.

Come on, Brit - ney, take it down. Make the mu - sic dance.

All my peo - ple 'round and 'round. Par - ty all night long.

Come on Brit - ney, lose con - trol. Watch you take it down.

Toxic

**Words & Music by Cathy Dennis, Christian Karlsson, Pontus Winnberg
& Henrik Jonback**

1. Ba - by, can't you see I'm call - ing,_____ a guy like you

Too high, can't come down.____
Too high, can't come down.____

Los-ing my head, spin-ning 'round and 'round.____
It's in the air and it's all a - round.____

Can you feel me now?

With a taste of your lips I'm

on a ride.   You're tox - ic,   I'm slip-ping un - der.   With the

taste of a poi - son pa - ra - dise,   I'm ad - dic - ted to you.   Don't you

know   that you're tox - ic?____   And I

love   what you do,   but you   know   that you're tox - ic.____

taste of a poi-son pa-ra-dise, I'm ad-dic-ted to you. Don't you

know that you're tox - ic.___ In-tox-i-cate me now_____ with your lov-ing now.___

___ I think I'm read-y now._____ I think I'm read-y now. In-tox-i-cate me now___

___ with your lov-ing now.___ I think I'm read-y now.___

Stronger

Words & Music by Max Martin & Rami

Verse 2:
...than I ever thought that
I could be, baby.
I used to go with the flow
Didn't really care 'bout me.
You might think
That I can't take it
But you're wrong.
'Cause now I'm...

Stronger *etc.*

The Only Exception

Words & Music by Joshua Farro & Hayley Williams

1. When I was young-er I saw my dad-dy cry_____ and curse at the wind.
2. May-be I'd know some-where deep in my soul_____ that love nev-er lasts.

only ex-cep-tion. Oh. Oh.

Hey. Oh.

I've got a tight grip on re-al-i-ty but
leav-in' in the morn-in' when you

I can't let go of what's in front of me here. I know you're
wake up. Leave me with some kind of proof it's not a

44

River Deep, Mountain High

Words & Music by Jeff Barry, Ellie Greenwich
& Phil Spector

Moderato with a strong beat

1. When I was a lit-tle girl____ I had a rag - doll,
(2.) ____ you have a pup - py

the on - ly doll____ I've ev - er owned.____
that al - ways fol - lowed you a - round?____

and I___ love you ba - by, like a ro - bin loves to sing.___

$E^\flat$

___ And I love you ba - by, like___ a

$B^\flat$

school - boy loves his pet,___ and I love you

D.C. al Fine

ba - by, ri - ver deep,___ moun - tain high.___

49

I Want To Hold Your Hand

Words & Music by John Lennon & Paul McCartney

1. Oh, yeah, I'll_____ tell you
(2.) please_____ say to

some - thing
me_____

I think you'll un - der - stand.
and let me be your man.

When
And

One Of Us

Words & Music by Eric Bazilian

God had a name___ what would it be and would you call it to his face
(2.) God had a face___ what would it look like and would you want to see___

1.If

Lucky

Words & Music by Jason Mraz, Colbie Caillat
& Tim Fagan

hear you in my dreams,___ I feel you whis-per a - cross the___
(F)breez-es through the trees___ move so pret-ty, you're all I

___ sea.___ I keep you with me in my___ heart. You make it
see.___ As the world keeps spin - ning___ 'round you'll

eas - i - er when___ life gets hard.___ }
hold me right___ here right now.___ } (BOTH) Luck - y I'm in___

___ love with my best friend.___ Luck - y to have___ been where I have been.___

62

One Love (People Get Ready)

Words & Music by Bob Marley & Curtis Mayfield

One love,— one heart.—

Let's get to-geth - er and feel all right.
Hear the chil-dren
As it was in the be-
I'm plead-ing to

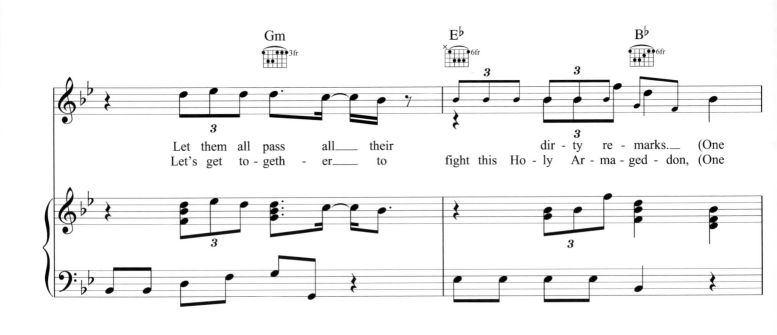

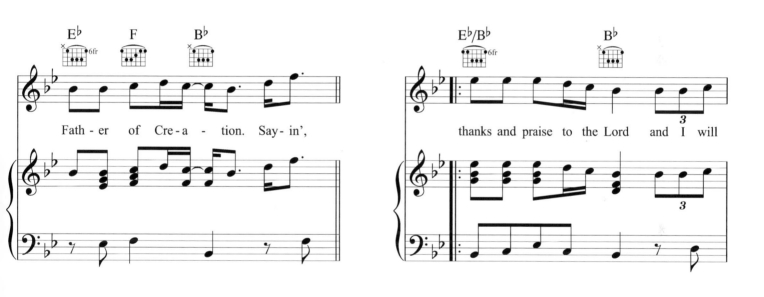

Teenage Dream

Words & Music by Max Martin, Lukasz Gottwald, Bonnie McKee,
Katy Perry & Benjamin Levin

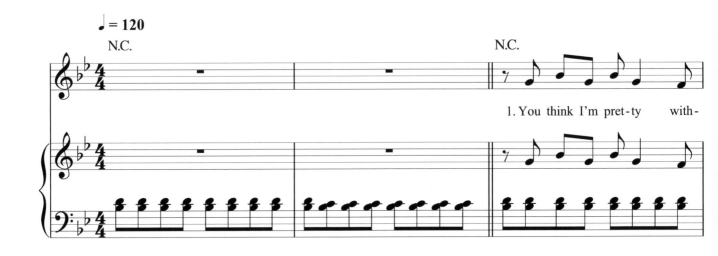

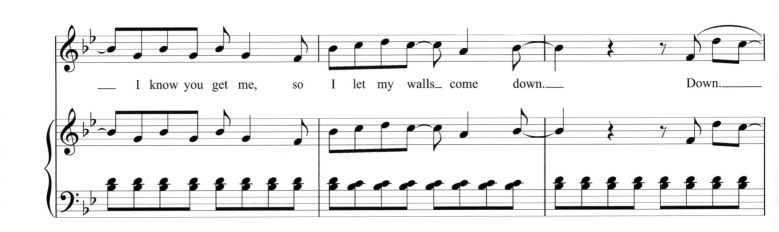

Forget You

Words & Music by Thomas Callaway, Philip Lawrence,
Peter Hernandez, Ari Levine & Christopher Brown

I see you driv-ing 'round town with the guy I love__ and I'm like,__ 'For-get you'!__

__ (Ooh, ooh, ooh.)__ I guess the change in my pock-et__ was-n't e-nough.__ I'm like,__

74

Marry You

Words & Music by Ari Levine, Peter Hernandez
& Phillip Lawrence

Hey, ba - by, I think I wan - na mar - ry you.____

Is it the look in your eyes____ or is it this

danc - ing juice?____ Who cares____ ba - by,____ I

think I wan - na mar - ry you.____

To Coda

1. Well, I
2. Oh,____

81

Hey, ba - by, I think I wan - na mar - ry you.

Is it the look in your eyes

or is it this danc - ing juice? Who cares

ba - by, I think I wan - na mar - ry you.

Sway

Words & Music by Pablo Beltran Ruiz

1. When ma-rim-ba rhy-thms

Valerie

Words & Music by Sean Payne, David McCabe, Abi Harding,
Boyan Chowdhury & Russel Pritchard

your gin - ger hair and the way you like to dress.

Oh, won't you come on o - ver? Stop mak - ing a fool out of me.

Why don't you come on o - ver Va -

- le - rie? Va - le - rie.

(Why don't you come on o - ver?) Va -

- - le - rie.___ Va - le - rie.___

To Coda

(Why don't you come on o - ver?) 2. Did you
4. Well, some -

have to go to jail,___ put your house on up for sale?___
- times___ I go out___ by my - self___ and I___

Just The Way You Are

Words & Music by Ari Levine, Bruno Mars, Philip Lawrence,
Peter Hernandez, Khari Cain & Khalil Walton

But ev-'ry time_ she asks_ me "Do_ I look o - kay?"_ I say:_

When I see your face,_

there's not a thing_ that I_ would change_ 'cause you're a - maz-

- ing_ just_ the way_ you are._

98

And when you smile,   the whole world stops

Dm

___ and stares__ for a while.___ 'Cause girl you're a - maz - ing___ just__

B♭

F

___ the way__ you are.___   Yeah.___

2. Her lips, her lips___ I could kiss them all___ day if___ she'd let me.

Dm

Her laugh, her laugh,___ she hates, but I___ think it's___ so sex - y.

B♭

She's so beau - ti - ful___ and I tell her ev - 'ry___

F

___ day.___

F

Oh,___ you know, you know, you know I'd nev - er

Dm

ask you to change.___ If per-fect's what you're search-ing for then just stay the same.___ So___

don't e - ven both - er ask - ing if___ you look___ o - kay,___ you know I'll

say:_____ When I see your face,___

there's not a thing___ that I___ would change___ 'cause you're a - maz-

-ing___ just___ the way___ you are.___

And when you smile,_ the whole world stops_

Dm

B♭

_ and stares_ for a while. 'Cause girl, you're a - maz - ing_ just_

F

_ the way_ you are._ The way_ you are,_

Dm

_ the way_ you are,_

girl, you're a - maz - ing _____ just _____ the way _____ you are. _____

When I see your face, _____

there's not a thing _____ that I _____ would change _____

'cause you're a - maz - ing _____ just _____

(I've Had) The Time Of My Life

Words & Music by Frankie Previte, John DeNicola
& Donald Markowitz

105

(M) 1. I've been wait-ing for so long,___ now I've fi-nal-ly found some-one to stand by

me.

(F) We saw the writ-ing on the wall___ as we
(F) bod - y and soul___ I want you

felt this ma - gi - cal___ fan - ta - sy.___
more than you'll ev - er know.___

(2° lower harmonies only)

(BOTH) Now with
(M) So we'll

106

(F) 2. With my owe it all to you,_ 'cause_

I've had the time of my life,_ and I've searched through ev - 'ry o - pen

door till I've found the_ truth_ and I owe it all to you._

23456789